by BRAD ANDERSON

Ravette London

This edition published by Ravette Ltd, 1986

Printed and bound in Great Britain for Ravette Limited,
3 Glenside Estate, Star Road, Partridge Green, Horsham, Sussex RH13 8RA
by Camelot Press Limited.

ISBN 0 948456 02 7

1-7-82

"Off! And never mind that 'why don't you sit in the kitchen' look!"

1-6-82

"Will you get out of here, Marmaduke...I almost unscrewed your nose!"

1-5-82
© 1981 United Feature Syndicate, Inc.

"I learned how to tie bows today!"

1-4-82
© 1981 United Feature Syndicate, Inc.

"Is this the bone you've been looking for?"

"You forgot to say goodbye to him."

"Sometimes Marmaduke hides his bubble gum behind his ear, Aunt Shirley."

"Does a large Great Dane live here?"

"Move over! I've read this page three times
and still don't know what it says!"

"Maybe fish don't like to eat bones, Marmaduke."

"I suggest you stay in your doghouse until Dottie gets over your eating up her casserole!"

"Hold your fire! It's Marmaduke
with a convoy!"

"A cat ran across the TV screen."

"...And no flipping the light switch off!"

"Let him in. I'd rather he came through the door than the window."

"We're playing beautician..."

"Hold it, you two...I'LL set the thermostat!"

"So THAT'S where our electric
blanket was!"

"We made a deal...if I pull him around the
block, he'll let me sit in my new easy chair."

"You'd better hurry! Marmaduke wants to see the dog cartoons!"

"Bad news, Casanova!"

"Thank goodness for remote control."

"It's nice you think so much of me,
but I can't drive like this!"

"He knows what laps are for."

"The interest rate will be
18%...17%...16...how about a flat 10%?!"

"Don't expect any help from me...
I'm in the doghouse myself!"

"I don't want to wake him, either...but
we HAVE to answer that robbery-in-progress."

"I'd better start shoveling."

"You wanted something?"

2-5

"Can't you wait until I'm out of the house
before you crawl in there?"

RAFFLE
WIN A
DOG

5¢

2-9

"We raffled you off, Marmaduke, but you
know how to find your way home again."

"You're forgetting something.
I'M the boss!"

"Three chocolate sodas, please...
one in a bowl!"

"SPOILSPORT!"

"I didn't know we were having breakfast in bed this morning."

"So?...I have bony knees!"

"Has anybody seen my winter hat
and sheepskin coat?"

"No wonder we couldn't sleep!"

"Maybe if you got home at a decent hour,
they wouldn't lock you out!"

"You might as well turn the motor off...
you know how expensive gas is!"

"I take it you're postponing your trip
until spring."

**"When will you learn that
neatness counts?!"**

"I can't explain it...whenever he barks,
the automatic garage door opens!"

"I don't know what you've done this time,
but that disguise won't fool anyone!"

2·24 © 1982 United Feature Syndicate, Inc.

"That's only the foothill...wait till it gets to the mountains!"

2·27 © 1982 United Feature Syndicate, Inc.

"Phil! Discipline him!"

"Marmaduke just LOVES grandmas!"

"It's the equivalent of a doggie bag from the finest restaurant in town!"

"Mom, I wish you wouldn't send Duke
for me in front of the guys!"

"Honest, Marmaduke, you're the only
dog in my life."

"If you hit Marmaduke with a snowball,
he hits you with a BLIZZARD!"

"Don't be impatient...you'll get your
gingerbread dog soon."

"There...I've solved the mystery
of the snoring coats!"

"We never disagree which way to go.
He goes his way and I go with him."

"You're right...they're not very good!"

"You'll never be fully paid for!"

3·13

© 1982 United Feature Syndicate, Inc.

"Watch him regain the will to live."

© 1982 United Feature Syndicate, Inc.

3·12

"Tell him the next time my hat blows off,
to let it blow!"

"Can't it wait until later? I'm too tired to play King Solomon!"

"See? The birds like him because he protects them!"

"Well, I'll be! Where did Marmaduke learn the secret handshake of the *Order of Eastern Mystics*?!"

"It isn't hungry! It just wants a drink!"

"Mom, he wants peanut butter and jelly on his bone!"

"It's your fault. You thought I had plenty of room!"

"Is this the only place where they can
come in out of the cold?"

"I wonder what the reigning monarch
wants us to do today?"

"Why can't we just be pals?!"

"Just when I got rid of that last batch of hats, we have another windy day!"

3·26

"Stop chasing the birds with that feeder...they'll find it on their own!"

3·30

"It's the animal shelter. Did you chase their dogcatcher out of town?"

3-29

"Not that chair, Mrs. Marsh...
it's Marmaduke's!"

4-1

"Whew! What he needs is a good dose of
spring fever!"

3·31

"May Fred look around? He's missing a
NO TRESPASSING sign."

4·3

"Guess what we spring clean next?!"

"He's no trouble. He does what he wants, and we do what he wants."

"It's uncanny how you always know when I'm in the shower!"

"The salesman would like to have that back."

"I did not get a bigger piece of pie than you!"

"I'm not taking my eyes off him...
there's no telling what kind of mischief
he's thinking up!"

"The obedience school is changing its
motto from 'No dog is untrainable' to
'Some dogs are hopeless!'"

"Wake up! Tell me this is only a
nightmare!"

"Never mind that cross-your-heart trick...
a beef patty is missing, and you're
the prime suspect!"

"Marmaduke's ready for his grapefruit."

"May I have that remote control? I'm tired
of dog food commercials."

"He doesn't get up unless it's something worthwhile."

"He's ASKING us to put him in there... I smell a mass escape plan!"

4·20

"Am I getting all this attention because you love me, or because the kids are in school?"

4·22

"He hid his bones in the 'old clothes' closet and they all smell of mothballs!"

4-21

"Who set the blanket on high?"

4-24

"Better shake hands with him...it's a
new trick he just learned!"

"Don't you ever WALK home?"

"Marmaduke gets upset if anyone talks
during a dog food commercial."

4·26

"Marmaduke is helping the early birds
find a worm!"

4.29

"Don't you even feel a *twinge* of guilt?"

4.28 © 1982 United Feature Syndicate, Inc.

"Marmaduke's letting them stay with him until they find a place of their own!"

5-1

"Do you still think you haven't spoiled him?"

"I'm sorry...I didn't know you don't like cigar smoke in the house!"

"Stop! Stop! No kisses while I'm working!"

"He's not trying to catch his tail...
he's looking for the designer label on
his new sweater."

"See what happens when you sleep out
in the bushes."

"Every time they scold you, you come over here and give me that ol' buddy stuff."

"I warn you...Marmaduke wants you to get up!"

"Hold the gossip until I get rid of ol'
MR. BIG EARS!"

"I gotta think of something that will
make Dottie mad enough to put me
in the doghouse."

"You won't believe this, but I was dragged six miles in the marathon race and won third place!"

"Brother Marmaduke has just proposed a sun roof for our clubhouse!"

"You wouldn't look so great either if you had been at the lodge meeting last night."

"Hey, I'm *not* Phil...I'm fragile."

"In case you didn't know, hammocks were not meant to be jumped on!"

"Mrs. Winslow! Our little Mitsy has a visitor. Would you care to know the rest?"

1-4-83

"Stop trying to hypnotize me into
giving up my chair!"

1-8-83

"Take your bone back. I don't
take bribes!"

"This is *not* my idea of cozy!"

"What he needs is a muzzle for his tail!"

"All I know is, he was chasing a squirrel..."

"We *could* have your dog license revoked, you know!"

"Marmaduke loves that dog food. It's a
200-wag dinner!"

"Mom! He's fluffing the couch again!"

"What other game do you know?"

"From now on, have the paperboy drop off *two* newspapers!"

"What's this about you talking back to him?"

"Dad should never have let Marmaduke take the lead!"

"Really...you and your scary
cartoon shows!"

"I once made the mistake of giving him
some scraps from my lunch!"

3·29

"He's after the 'hubcap hijacker' and has a
warrant to search your doghouse!"

3·28

"Phil, you'd better get up!"

"May I?"

"They're not *my* cold feet."

1-25 © 1983 United Feature Syndicate, Inc.

"He's the only dog I know that can sleep with one eye open for cats."

1-27 © 1983 United Feature Syndicate, Inc.

"I'd be willing to pay *you* not to bring him in here again."

"He's guilty about something...and I'm afraid to find out what it is."

"I said, have a drink...not a shower!"

"And now, with an opposing viewpoint on
the new leash law..."

"Marmaduke's not making toast...he's just
warming his ears and nose!"

"A police car in our backyard. Marmaduke, you sure can ruin my day!"

FIRST AIDE

"Come on down, Marmaduke...we have to practice taking off bandages, too!"

"That was a short walk...just thirty seconds!"

"Nope! Your rubber ball isn't under that chair!"

"They want you to be their mascot."

"I can't believe this! I just had all the wheels balanced!"

2·9

"Yep! Marmaduke's there to greet
me...don't stop the bus until I get my knee
pads, elbow pads and helmet adjusted!"

2·12

"Oh, no, you don't! We're not having any
live-ins here!"

"Will you hold this a moment, sir, while I tie my shoe?"

"Don't you ever have afternoon dates?"

"Cross your heart! I'm not receiving stolen goods!"

"You're our patient, Marmaduke, and you have to wait an hour before we can see you."

"It's uncanny the way he heads for the refrigerator when he walks in his sleep!"

"I see you edging back over here again...but you're not coming up here on the couch!"

2-18

"I think he's in love again."

2·21

"I don't know what's so awful about getting your feet wet!"

"The money wasted on obedience schools
cannot be taken as a tax loss!"

"No! I'm not going to turn up the heat!"

"He's been suspiciously well-behaved
all day!"

"Go keep somebody else company!"

"I'll be glad when winter is over and he goes back to sleeping in his doghouse!"

"We have our own insect control... Marmaduke barks at the house and they all disappear!"

"Hurry up! I have to brush my teeth!"

"Gee! I never have any problem collecting on my paper route!"

"I didn't bring him. I thought you did!"

"But, doctor...your vacation doesn't start until tomorrow!"

3-8

"Who would think *we* would ever have
an energy crisis?"

3-9

"Nothing much...just an elephant missing
from the circus!"

"Couldn't you wait until I get home to let me know you got into trouble today?"

"You *can't* help...it's against union rules!"

"You mean, *he* has to approve before you buy?"

"He's been more normal than usual today!"

"I let him carry my books, but never my lunch."

"There must be *something* about you that's deductible!"

3-16

"This is for the head of the house...er...let
me rephrase that!"

Circus
Today
5¢

3-21

BRAD ANDERSON

"Now...Marmaduke!"

BEWARE !!! DOG ON PREMISES

KEEP OUT

3-22

"He heard me mention spring cleaning!"

3-23

"I'm sorry, but when we have guests, Marmaduke thinks he's on the entertainment committee!"

3-24

"What did *you* do to get in the doghouse...if you'll forgive the expression?"

3-25

"Aren't you going to stand while they play the National Anthem, Pop?"

"Of course he's not hungry...he's already eaten my slippers, pipe and newspaper!"

"What a waste of money it was buying them each a jogging suit!"

"You call *that* the pitter-patter of little feet?"

"He isn't very subtle, is he?"

4·13 © 1983 United Feature Syndicate, Inc.

"Remember, Marmaduke...tell him when I say *no*, I mean *no*!"

4·14 © 1983 United Feature Syndicate, Inc.

"She caught him running around with a French poodle!"

"All week, you want to go for a walk at
10 a.m., but Saturday you want to
go at 5 a.m.!"

"I refuse to tell her you're not home! If you
are breaking up, tell her yourself!"

4.20

"Don't tell me...let me guess...you took
Marmaduke to the vet."

4·21

"It's the dog show about the loving
cup you *borrowed*!"

"Who gave you permission to put your
bones in with my roast?"

"If there's one thing I can't stand, it's a
male chauvinist backseat driver."

Other cartoon books published by Ravette

Garfield paperbacks

No. 1	Garfield The Great Lover	£1.50
No. 2	Garfield Why Do You Hate Mondays?	£1.50
No. 3	Garfield Does Pooky Need You?	£1.50
No. 4	Garfield Admit It, Odie's OK!	£1.50
No. 5	Garfield Two's Company	£1.50
No. 6	Garfield What's Cooking?	£1.50
No. 7	Garfield Who's Talking?	£1.50
No. 8	Garfield Strikes Again	£1.50
No. 9	Garfield Here's Looking At You	£1.50
No. 10	Garfield We Love You Too	£1.50
No. 11	Garfield Here We Go Again	£1.50
No. 12	Garfield Life and Lasagne	£1.50

Garfield Landscapes

Garfield The All-Round Sports Star	£1.95
Garfield The Irresistible	£1.95
Garfield On Vacation	£1.95
Garfield Weighs In	£1.95
Garfield I Hate Monday	£1.95
Garfield Special Delivery	£1.95
Garfield The Incurable Romantic	£1.95

Introducing Snake	£2.50
Marmaduke Super dog	£2.50
Frank and Ernest	£1.95

All these books are available at your local bookshop or newsagent, or can be ordered direct from the publisher. Just tick the titles you require and fill in the form below. Prices and availability subject to change without notice.

Ravette Limited, 3 Glenside Estate, Star Road, Partridge Green, Horsham, West Sussex, RH13 8RA.

Please send a cheque or postal order, and allow the following for postage and packing. UK 45p for one book, plus 20p for each additional book ordered.

Name ....

Address ....

....